Percy the Park Keeper
Activity Book

NICK BUTTERWORTH

Collins

An Imprint of HarperCollins*Publishers*

Toboggan Run

Three of Percy's friends are having a race down the toboggan run but only one of them makes it to the finishing line.
Trace the paths and work out which mouse wins.

FINISH

Crossing the Icy Pond

Percy wants a cup of tea but the mice have got his cup and saucer. Can you help the mice carry the cup and saucer across the icy pond to Percy without stepping on the cracks or falling into the icy water?

Dot-to-Dot

Percy is very busy today.
Join the dots to find out what he's doing.

Odd One Out

Percy is collecting balloons.
See how many you can match by
colour, then spot the odd one out.

5

Percy's Puzzle Trail

The squirrel, the fox and the badger are helping Percy clear up the park. Follow the path each animal takes – if there's something blocking your path, you've gone wrong.

Along the way can you see:

• Who finds the saw and helps Percy cut the logs?

• Who finds the spade and helps Percy clear up the soil?

• Who finds the watering can and waters the tree for Percy?

6

Percy's Word Search

See if you can find the ten words listed below that are hidden in this puzzle. Look for words which go from top to bottom, or from left to right, or diagonally.

Tree
Badger
Birds
Rabbits
Owl

Fox
Percy
Leaf
Mice
Mole

```
T O C S M I A W
R A B B I T S B
E H A Y C N V I
E S D L E A F R
N U G I H F M D
O P E R C Y O S
H W R A Q K L X
Z I L P S U E T
```

Tangled Kites

Percy's friends are flying their kites, but the strings
are all tangled up. Can you untangle the strings
and see who each kite belongs to?

Colour by Numbers

Colour in each shape using this colour code:

1 = blue   2 = green   3 = orange   4 = pink   5 = brown   6 = black

Percy's Hut

Can you find these objects in the picture above
and write their names in the crossword below?

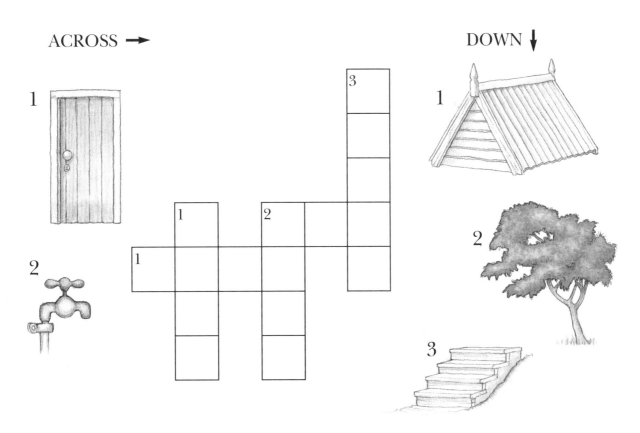

ACROSS ➡

DOWN ⬇

Journey Around The Park

Go forwards. Collect wheelbarrow and pick up leaves.

Go forwards and help Percy.

Go back. Pick up the rubbish on the path.

Miss a turn. Play on the roundabout.

You will need a dice and one counter for each player. Play by rolling the dice and moving along the squares. Have fun visiting Percy in the park and help him with a job or two. The first to reach the finishing line is the winner.

START

FINISH

24

25

26

27

Miss a turn.
Visit Percy's
hut for tea.

28

29

30

31

32

33

34

Go back.
Help rescue the
rabbit from
the well.

35

46

Go forwards. Swing
on the rope
tied to the tree.

45

44

36

Go forwards.
Trim the hedge
as you go.

37

43

Fallen tree.
Go back and
fetch the saw.

42

41

40

39

38

Spot the Difference

There are eight differences between these pictures.
See if you can spot them.

Now you can colour in the pictures.

Pawprints in the Mud

Mouse

Fox

Badger

Rabbit

Percy carried four of his friends across the river in his wheelbarrow. When they reached the river bank the animals leapt out into the mud and ran off. Follow the pawprints and see how each animal arrived home.

Dot-to-Dot

Percy has spent the day clipping hedges in the maze. Use a squiggly line to join the dots and see what shapes he has made.

Keeping Warm in Winter

What does Percy wear when it's cold?
Find the items of clothing in the picture above and
write their names in the crossword below.

ACROSS ➡   DOWN ⬇

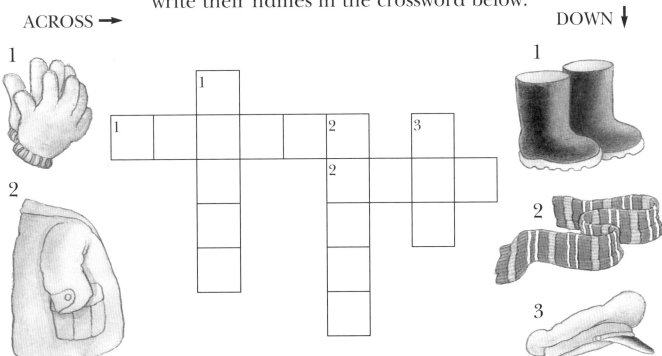

The Maze Race

You will need a dice and one counter for each player. Play by rolling the dice and moving along the squares. Sometimes the square will have a little path that will lead you forwards or backwards through the maze. The first player to reach the finish is the winner. Have an extra turn if you throw a six.

START 1 2 3 4 5 6 7 8 9 10 11 12 13 14 15

16
17
18
19
20
21
22
23
24
25
26 27 28 29 30 FINISH

Life in the Oak Tree

Count how many moles, squirrels, hedgehogs, rabbits, mice and birds you can see in the oak tree and write the number in each of the boxes below.

Moles ☐

Squirrels ☐

Hedgehogs ☐

Rabbits ☐

Mice ☐

Birds ☐

Now add up all the numbers to find the grand total of animals living in the oak tree.

TOTAL ☐

Answers

Page 2 **Toboggan Run**

Page 3 **Crossing the Icy Pond**

Page 4 **Dot-to-Dot**
Percy is pushing a wheelbarrow.

Page 5 **Odd One Out**
There are 4 blue balloons, 4 red, 4 pink, 4 yellow, 4 green, but only 1 purple. The purple balloon is the odd one out.

Page 6 **Percy's Puzzle Trail**
The badger finds the saw and helps Percy cut the logs. The fox finds the spade and helps Percy clear up the soil. The rabbit finds the watering can and waters the tree.

Page 8 **Percy's Word Search**

Page 9 **Tangled Kites**
The rabbit is holding kite 4
The mole is holding kite 3
The badger is holding kite 1
The fox is holding kite 2

Page 11 **Percy's Hut**

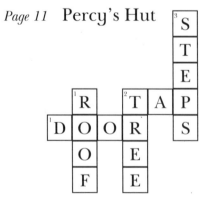

Page 14 **Spot the Difference**

Page 18 **Dot-to-Dot**
Percy has made a teapot and a hen.

Page 19 **Keeping Warm in Winter**

Pages 22/23 **Life in the Oak Tree**
21 animals live in the oak tree.

1 Mole	3 Squirrels
1 Hedgehog	3 Rabbits
3 Mice	10 Birds

First published in Great Britain by HarperCollins Publishers Ltd in 1996
ISBN 0 00 136040 X   1 3 5 7 9 10 8 6 4 2